Power Maths

Year 1 Practice Book

C000256385

What would you like to learn to do better in maths this term? Write it here.

This book belongs to _____ .

My class is _____ .

Pearson

Contents

I can't wait to have a go at these things!

It's time for the next part of our maths journey!

How to use this book

Do you remember how to use this Practice Book?

Use the Textbook first to learn how to solve this type of problem.

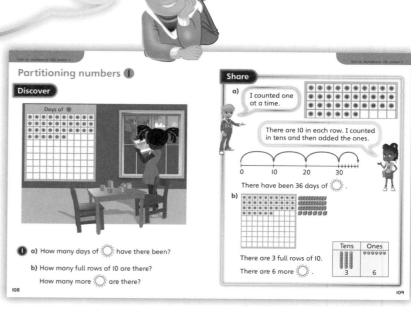

This shows you which Textbook page to use.

Have a go at questions by yourself using this Practice Book. Use what you have learned.

Challenge questions make you think hard!

Questions with this light bulb make you think differently.

Reflect

Each lesson ends with a Reflect question so you can show how much you have learned.

Show what you have done in My Power Points at the back of this book.

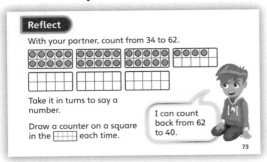

My journal

At the end of a unit your teacher will ask you to fill in My journal.

This will help you show how much you can do now that you have finished the unit.

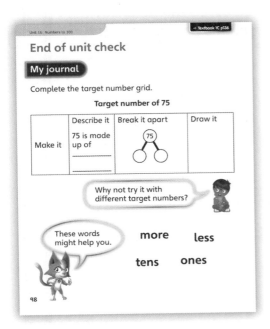

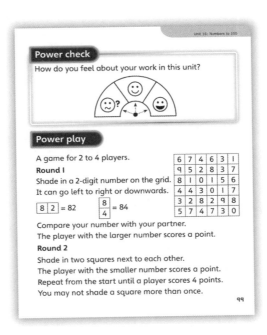

→ Textbook 1C p8

Counting in 10s, 5s and 2s

1 **a)** Match the count to the objects.

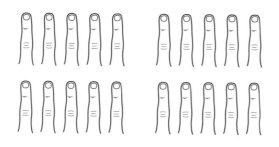 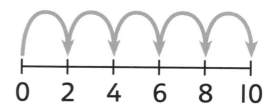

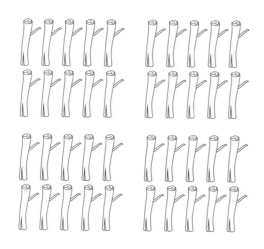 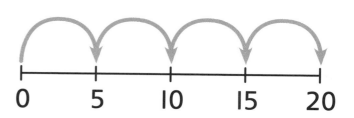

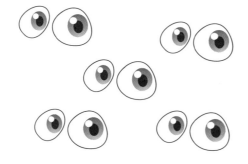 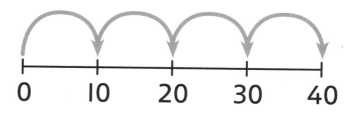

b) There are ☐ fingers.

There are ☐ sticks.

There are ☐ eyes.

2

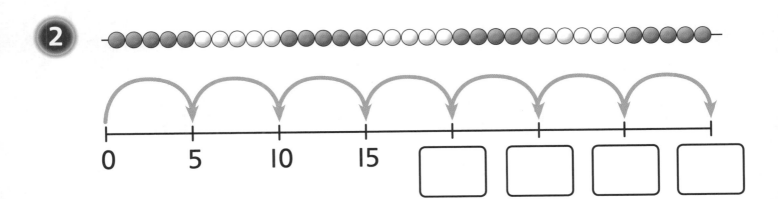

There are ☐ beads.

3 Filip is counting the ◇.

Explain his mistake.

5, 10, 15, 25, 30, 35. There are 35 ◇.

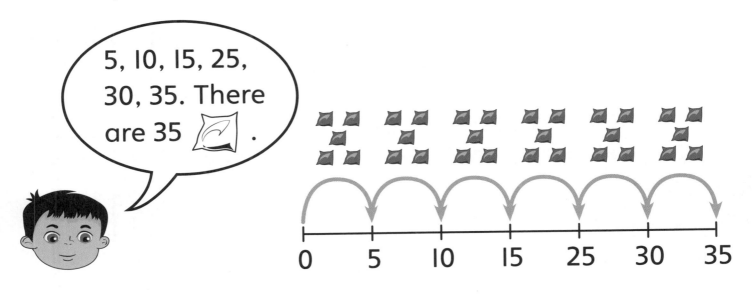

Filip's mistake is...

_____

_____

4 **a)** Count in 2s. Circle all the numbers you say.

CHALLENGE

b) Count in 5s. Colour in all the numbers you say.

c) Which numbers have both a circle and a colour?

_____

1	2	3	4	5	6	7	8	9	10
11	12	13	14	15	16	17	18	19	20
21	22	23	24	25	26	27	28	29	30

d) What other numbers would have both a circle and a colour if you counted on?

_____

Reflect

How would you count the wheels on 5 bicycles?

_____

_____

_____

Making equal groups

1 Complete the number sentences.

a) There are 5 groups of ☐ candles.

b) There are ☐ groups of ☐ lollies.

c) There are ☐ groups of 2 gloves.

d) There are ☐ groups of 2 hats.

e) There are ☐ groups of 2 scarves.

2 **a)** Draw dots to make 3 equal groups.

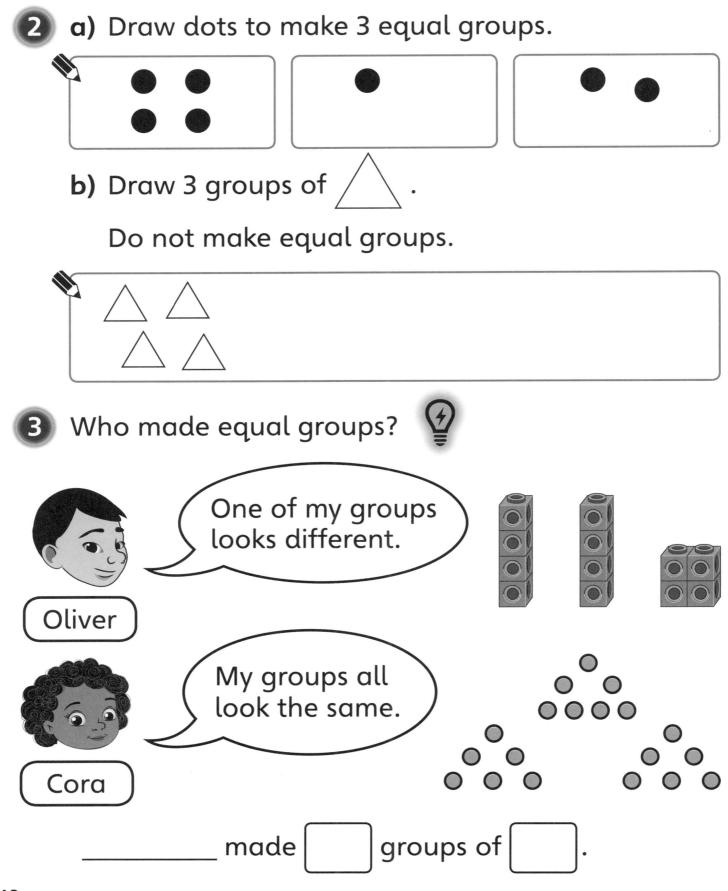

b) Draw 3 groups of △.

Do not make equal groups.

3 Who made equal groups?

One of my groups looks different.

Oliver

My groups all look the same.

Cora

_____ made ☐ groups of ☐.

Tell a story about the equal groups or the unequal groups.

_____

_____

Reflect

Use  and ◯ .

Make equal groups of ⬚ .

Make unequal groups of ◯ .

Draw your groups below.

Equal groups	Unequal groups

→ Textbook 1C p16

Adding equal groups

1 **a)** How many wheels are there?

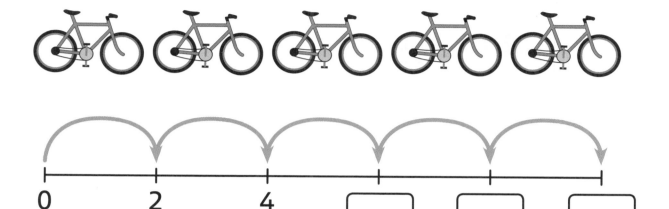

$2 + 2 + 2 + 2 + 2 = \boxed{}$

There are $\boxed{}$ wheels.

b) How many spots are there?

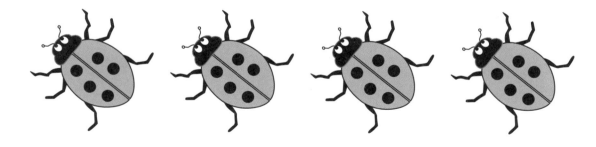

$5 + 5 + 5 + 5 = \boxed{}$

There are $\boxed{}$ spots.

Each snowman's eyes and mouth are made of buttons.

How many buttons are needed for 3 snowmen?

☐ + ☐ + ☐ = ☐

☐ buttons are needed for 3 snowmen.

3 Complete the table.

Dice	[die]	[2 dice]	[3 dice]	[4 dice]
Score	5	5 + 5 = 10	5 + 5 + 5 = ☐	_____ = ☐

4 Complete the number lines and the additions.

a)

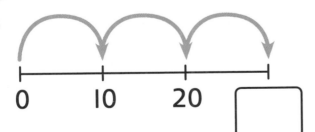

0   10   20   ☐

10 + 10 + 10 = ☐

b)

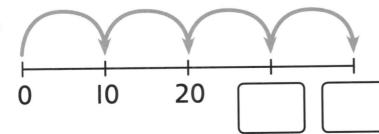

0   10   20   ☐   ☐

10 + 10 + 10 + 10 = ☐

13

5

CHALLENGE

Oliver: I have more stickers as my groups are bigger.

Anna: I have more stickers as I have more groups.

Who is right?

Reflect

I can work out how many shells there are by...

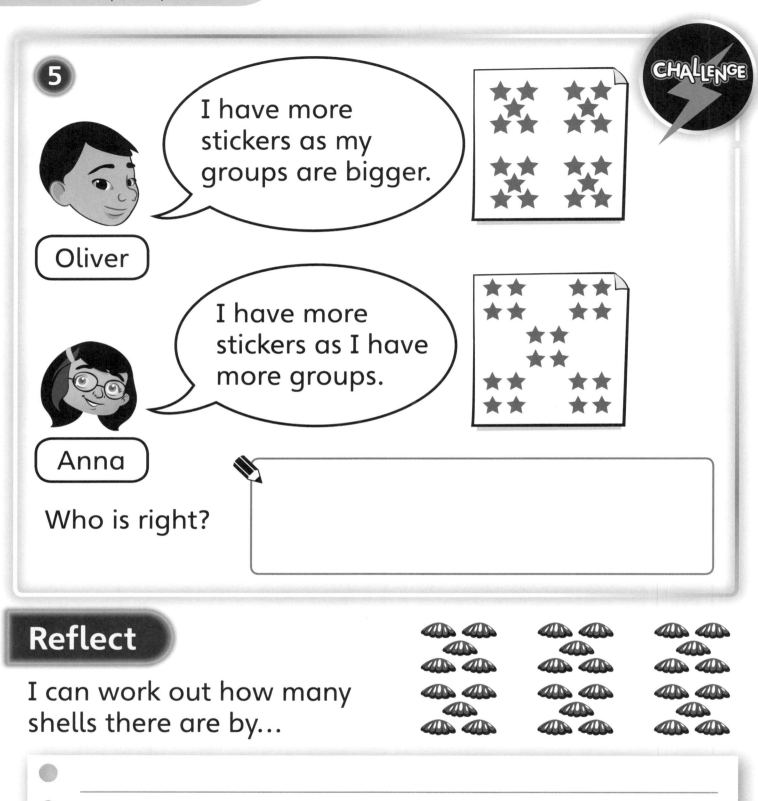

Making simple arrays

1 **a)**

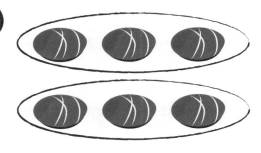

There are ☐

in each row.

There are ☐ rows.

b)

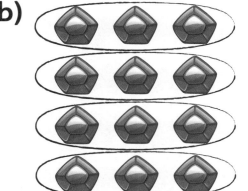

There are ☐

in each row.

There are ☐ rows.

2 Match the array to the descriptions.

△ ┊ △ ┊ △ ┊ △
△ ┊ △ ┊ △ ┊ △

4 columns.

2 in each column.

△ ┊ △ ┊ △
△ ┊ △ ┊ △
△ ┊ △ ┊ △
△ ┊ △ ┊ △

4 columns.

3 in each column.

△ ┊ △ ┊ △ ┊ △
△ ┊ △ ┊ △ ┊ △
△ ┊ △ ┊ △ ┊ △

3 columns.

4 △ in each column.

3 Complete the number line and the addition for the array.

 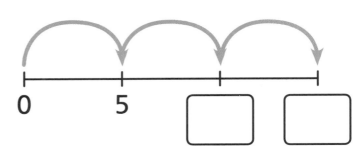

0   5   [ ]   [ ]

[ ] + [ ] + [ ] = [ ]

There are [ ] stars.

4 Tim and Kat are making arrays.

Who has made a mistake?

Tim

Kat

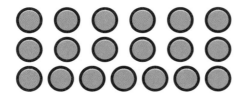

_____ has made a mistake because

_____

_____

5 Draw dots to complete the array.

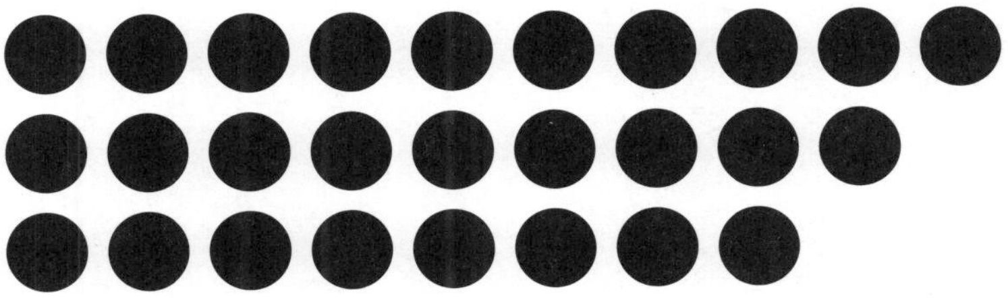

CHALLENGE

How many more dots did you draw? ☐

Reflect

Complete the number line and write the addition for this array.

Will you count the rows or the columns?

0

_____

_____

→ Textbook 1C p24

Making doubles

1 Circle the dominoes that show doubles.

2 Draw ◯ to complete the doubles.

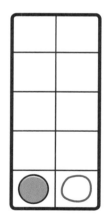 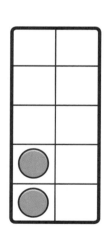 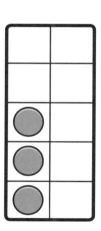 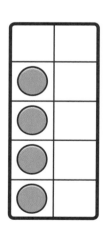 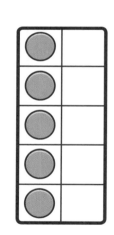

Double 1 is ☐.

Double 2 is ☐.

Double 3 is ☐.

Double ☐ is ☐.

Double ☐ is ☐.

3 Match each card to its double.

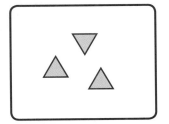 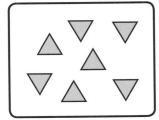 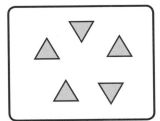 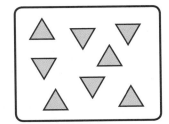

   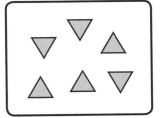

4 Complete the sentences.

a)

Double 4 is ☐.

c)

2 is double ☐.

b)

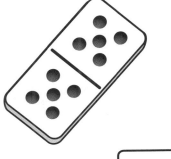

10 is double ☐.

d)

Double ☐ is ☐.

5 Double each number in the bubbles.

CHALLENGE

① ② ③ ④ ⑤ ⑥ ⑦ ⑧ ⑨ 10

Colour each double you make in the grid.

1	2	3	4	5	6	7	8	9	10
11	12	13	14	15	16	17	18	19	20

What do you notice?

_____

_____

Reflect

How many doubles do you know?

Ring the number and write its double underneath.

	1	2	3	4	5
Double:	2	4			
	6	7	8	9	10
Double:					

Solving word problems – multiplication

1 **a)**

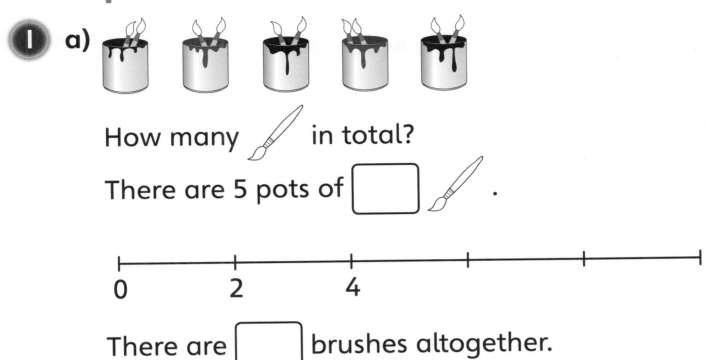

How many ✏ in total?

There are 5 pots of ☐ ✏ .

There are ☐ brushes altogether.

b) Ruben is sorting pencils into 6 pots.

He puts 5 pencils into each pot.

How many pencils are there in 6 pots?

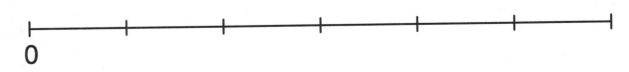

There are ☐ pencils altogether.

2 Match the question to the number line.

How many ◯ ?

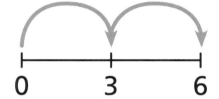

0   3   6

How many ☐ ?

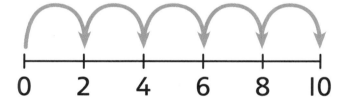

0   2   4   6   8   10

How many △ ?

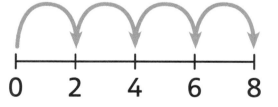

0   2   4   6   8

3 One more row is added to this array.

How many dots are there in total now?

There are ☐ dots in total.

CHALLENGE

4 **a)** ◯ is double ☆ .

☆ = 7, so ◯ = ☐ .

b) ☐ is double ♡ .

☐ = 10, so ♡ = ☐ .

Reflect

Make up a question for this number line.

You could make it about equal groups.

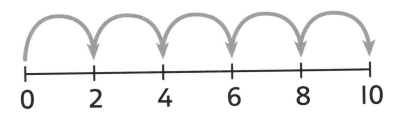

_____

_____

_____

End of unit check

My journal

This is double 10.

Joe

This is 10 groups of 2.

Sara

I can see it as 2 groups of 10.

Poppy

- Joe is right because _____
- _____
- _____
- Sara is right because _____
- _____
- _____
- Poppy is right because _____
- _____
- _____

Power check

How do you feel about your work in this unit?

Power play

Colour the squares to make different arrays.

Make sure every array you colour is different.

Colour an array yellow.

Colour a different array blue.

Colour a different array red.

Colour a different array black.

How many squares are blank?

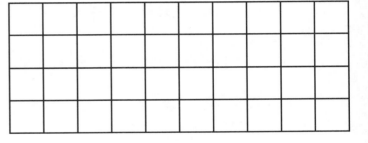

Try again.

Can you colour all the squares with 4 different arrays?

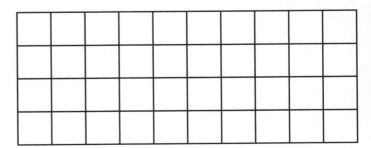

→ Textbook 1C p36

Making equal groups

1 **a)** The farmer puts 2 horses in each horsebox.

There are 8 horses in total.

How many horseboxes does the farmer need?

The farmer needs ☐ horseboxes with 2 horses each.

b) The farmer puts 3 sheep in each pen.

There are 15 sheep altogether.

How many pens does the farmer need?

The farmer needs ☐ pens of 3 sheep.

2 There are 18 bees altogether. How many groups of 3 bees are there?

There are ☐ groups of 3 bees.

3 Join each set of counters to the correct description.

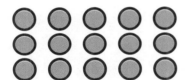

10 has been put into groups of 5.

There are 15 counters in groups of 3.

This is 15 sorted into groups of 5.

10 is sorted into groups of 2.

4 These children have 20 cubes each.

Which children made equal groups?

Tick the cubes in equal groups.

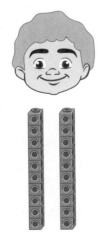

5 Show different ways to colour equal groups.

CHALLENGE

There are ☐ groups of ☐ .

There are ☐ groups of ☐ .

Reflect

There are 18 paper clips altogether.

How many chains of paper clips can Jed make that are the same length as this one?

Making equal groups ❷

1 Complete the sentences.

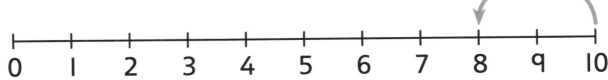

There are 10 shoes.

There are ☐ groups of 2 shoes.

2 a) There are 15 .

Luke puts 5 in each pot.

How many pots will he fill?

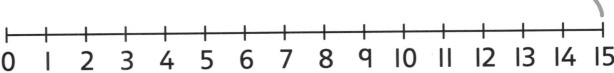

There are ☐ groups of 5.

Luke fills ☐ pots.

29

b) Cora has 25 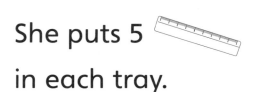 .

She puts 5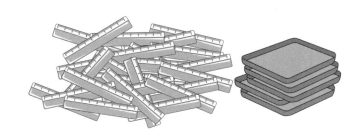

in each tray.

How many trays does Cora fill?

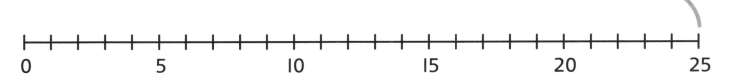

There are ☐ groups of 5.

Cora fills ☐ trays.

3 Children use sticks to make this flower pattern.

Ella has 40 sticks.

How many flower patterns like this can she make?

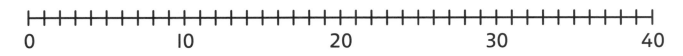

Ella has ☐ groups of 10 sticks.

She can make ☐ flower patterns.

4 Two people can sit in one go-kart.

Complete the table.

CHALLENGE

Number of people	Number line	How many groups of 2?
4	0 1 2 3 4 5 6 7 8 9 10	☐ groups of 2
8	0 1 2 3 4 5 6 7 8 9 10	☐ groups of 2
10	0 1 2 3 4 5 6 7 8 9 10	☐ groups of 2

Do you notice a pattern?

Reflect

30 pens are put into groups of 10.

There are ☐ groups of ☐ pens.

Explain how you found the answer.

→ Textbook 1C p44

Sharing equally

1 Share the toy cars equally between the children.

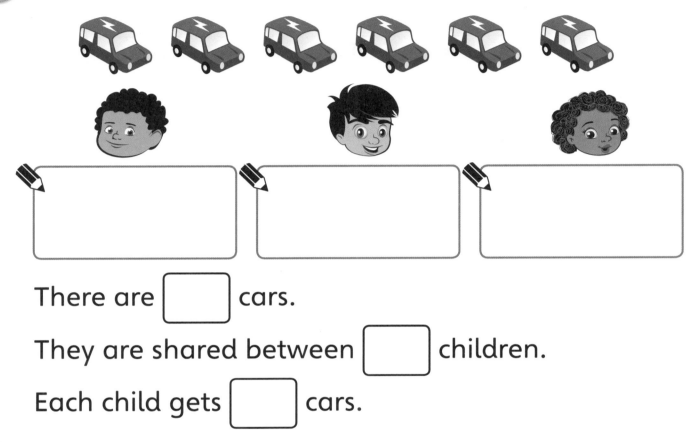

There are ☐ cars.

They are shared between ☐ children.

Each child gets ☐ cars.

2 Share the dinosaurs equally between the children.

There are ☐ dinosaurs.

They are shared between ☐ children.

Each child gets ☐ dinosaurs.

3 **a)** Two children share 18 cards equally between them for a game.

How many cards will each child get?

18 shared between 2 is ☐.

Each child gets ☐ cards.

b) One more child joins them and they have to share again.

Which sentence is correct?

A

Each child will get fewer than before.

B

Each child will get more than before.

C

Each child will get the same as before.

Explain your answer.

I think _____ is correct because _____

_____

_____ .

CHALLENGE

4 There are some marbles in a bag.

The marbles are shared between 4 children.

Each child gets more than 2 marbles, but fewer than 5 marbles.

How many marbles were in the bag?

Find two answers.

Answer 1:

There were ☐ marbles.

Answer 2:

There were ☐ marbles.

Reflect

I want to share 20 cherries between the cakes.

Explain how the cook can use counters or cubes to work out how many cherries should go on each cake.

Sharing equally ❷

1 Zac shares these carrots between his rabbits.

How many carrots are there for each rabbit?

a)
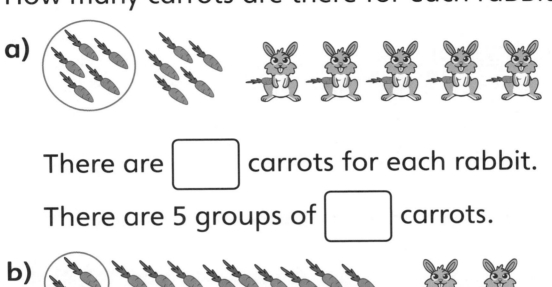

There are ☐ carrots for each rabbit.

There are 5 groups of ☐ carrots.

b)

There are ☐ carrots for each rabbit.

There are 2 groups of ☐ carrots.

2 How many lettuce leaves are there for each tortoise?

Each tortoise gets ☐ leaves.

There are 4 groups of ☐ leaves.

3 **a)** Match the groups that help you share between the people.

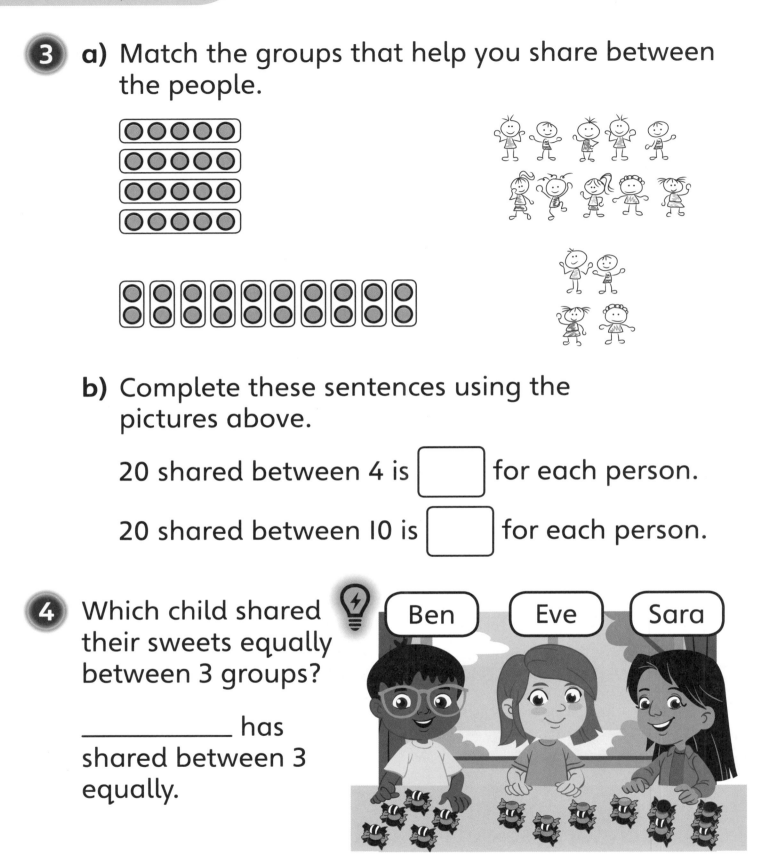

b) Complete these sentences using the pictures above.

20 shared between 4 is ☐ for each person.

20 shared between 10 is ☐ for each person.

4 Which child shared their sweets equally between 3 groups?

Ben   Eve   Sara

_____ has shared between 3 equally.

Explain the mistakes to your partner.

CHALLENGE

5 I shared some cakes equally between some plates.

This is what one of the plates looks like now.

I filled more than 6 plates, but fewer than 10 plates.

How many cakes did I start with?

Find three answers.

Answer 1: I had ☐ cakes.

Answer 2: I had ☐ cakes.

Answer 3: I had ☐ cakes.

I will use ◯ to help.

Reflect

● I can share 8 cubes between 4 people equally by

→ Textbook 1C p52

Solving word problems – division

1 Leo has 10 toy cars.

How many can he fill?

Leo can fill ☐  .

2 Jade collects stickers to go in this sticker book.

Jade won 25 stickers.

How many rows does she fill in her book?

Jade fills ☐ rows.

3 Eva    Toby

Toby shares his between 4 shelves.

Eva shares her between 3 shelves.

Who has more on each shelf?

_____ has more 🧸 on each shelf.

4 There are 14 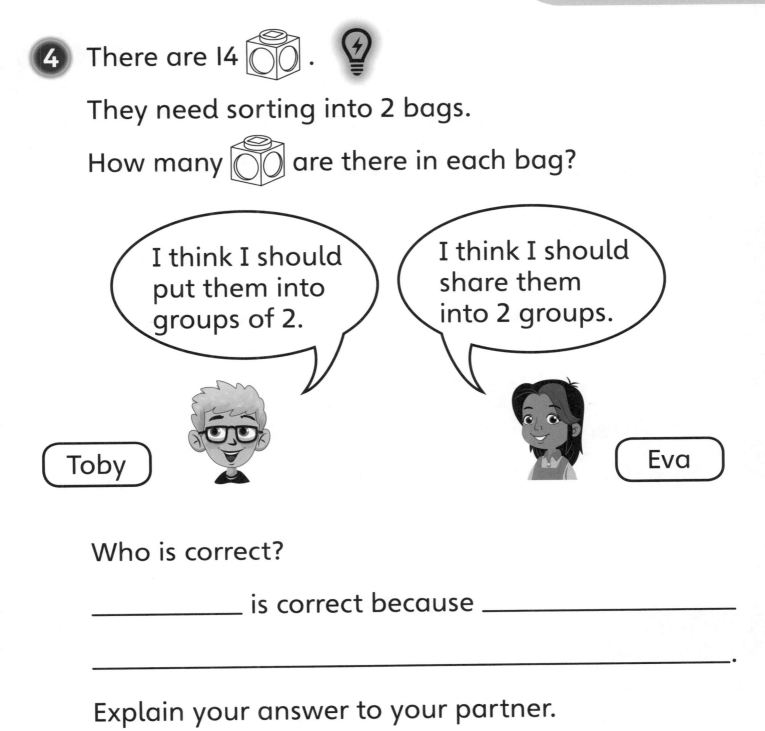 .

They need sorting into 2 bags.

How many are there in each bag?

I think I should put them into groups of 2.

Toby

I think I should share them into 2 groups.

Eva

Who is correct?

_____ is correct because _____

_____.

Explain your answer to your partner.

5 ○○○○○○○○○○○○○○○○○○○○

CHALLENGE

Share these counters into 5 groups.

Then share each group into 2 groups.

a) How many groups do you end up with?

There are ☐ groups.

b) How many counters will be in each group?

There are ☐ counters in each group.

Reflect

Which questions make equal groups?

Which questions use equal sharing?

Which question was the hardest?

- Question ☐ was the hardest because _____

_____

End of unit check

My journal

3 boys share 15 teddy bears equally.
2 girls share 12 teddy bears equally.

The boys say, 'We get more each because we have more in total.'

The girls say, 'We get more each because there are only 2 of us.'

Who is correct? Explain your answer.

Would your answer be the same if the boys had 18 teddy bears?

- _____
- _____
- _____

These words might help you.

group   **equal**

share   **equally**

total

Power check

How do you feel about your work in this unit?

Power puzzle

Liam drew two straight lines to split these dots into equal groups.

Draw two straight lines in each box so that the counters are split into equal groups.

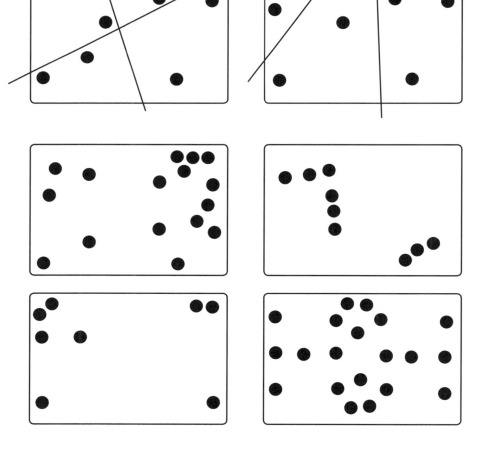

Finding halves

1 Draw a line to split each shape in half.

  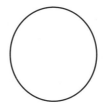 

2 a) Colour half of each square.

 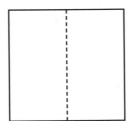 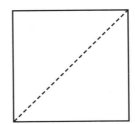 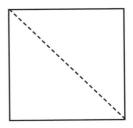

b) Colour half of each shape in 4 different ways.

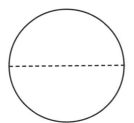 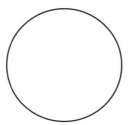 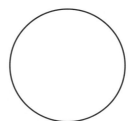 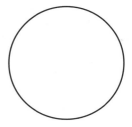

I can split the circle in half in lots of different ways.

3 Tick the shapes which are half shaded.

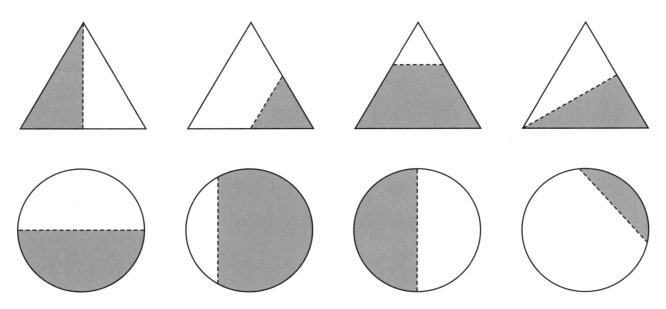

4 Match two halves that make a whole.

You can make four shapes.

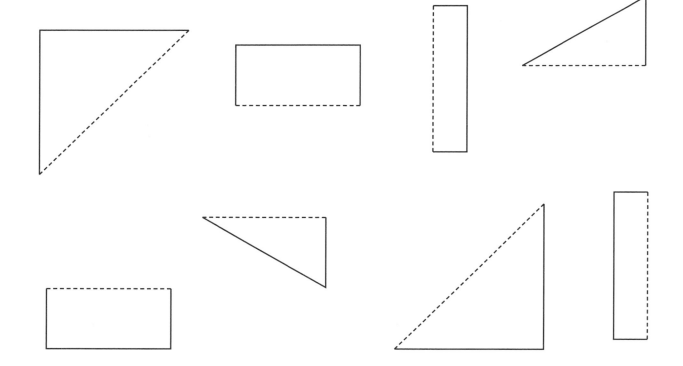

5 Match each shape to the correct words.

   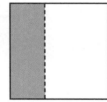

| less than half shaded | exactly half shaded | more than half shaded |

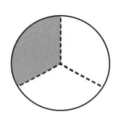 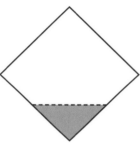 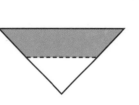 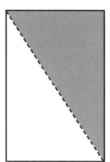

Reflect

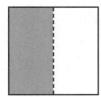   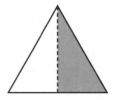

Which is the odd one out?

Why?

→ Textbook 1C p64

Finding halves ❷

1 A group of children splits into two halves.

How many in each half?

a)

Half of 8 children is ☐ children.

b)

Half of ☐ children is ☐ children.

2 Colour half of each group.

a)

b)

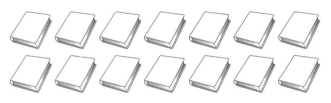

c)

d)

3 Complete the sentences.

Colour or draw lines on the pictures to help you.

a)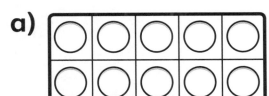

Half of 10 is ⬜.

c)

⬜ is half of 4.

b)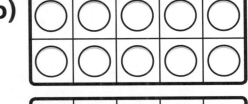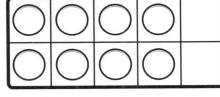

⬜ is half of 18.

d)

Half of 6 is ⬜.

4 Colour half of each shape.

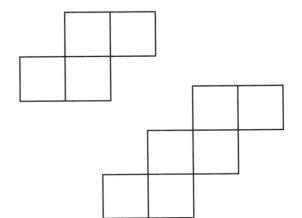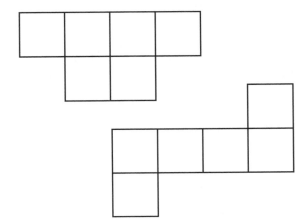

47

5 What are the values of and ?

 is half of  .

 + = 9

 = ☐

△ = ☐

I will pick a number to start with for ▲ . I can change it if it doesn't work.

Reflect

I can find half of 12 by _____

_____

_____

_____

Finding quarters ❶

❶ There are 4 painters.

They each paint a quarter of the wall.

Draw lines to split the wall into quarters.

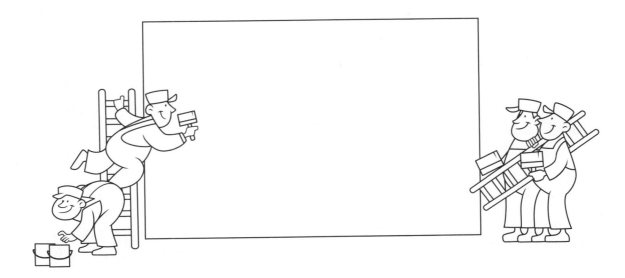

2 Colour a quarter of each shape.

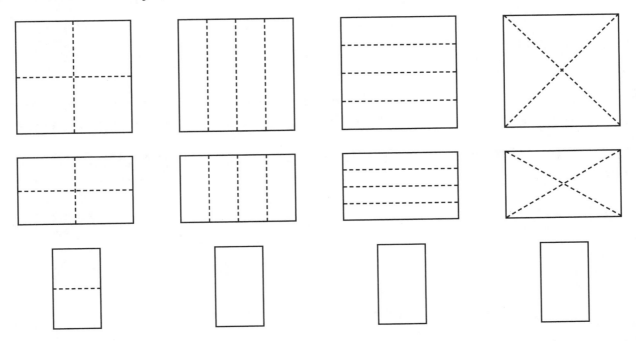

3 Tick the shapes with a quarter shaded.

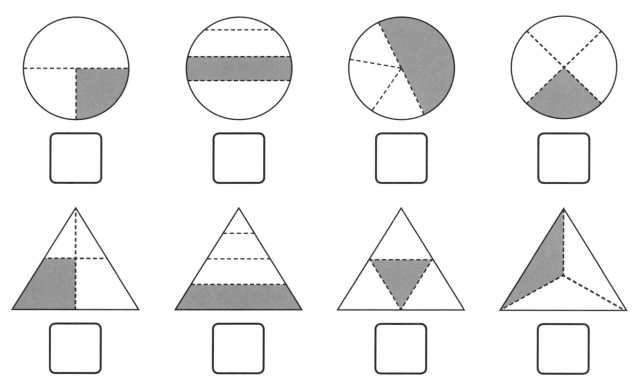

4 Match each shape to the correct words.

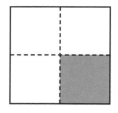 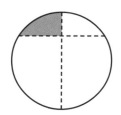 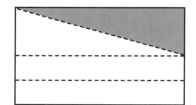 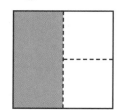

| less than a quarter shaded | exactly a quarter shaded | more than a quarter shaded |

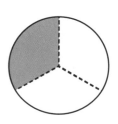 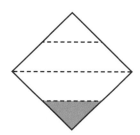 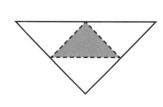 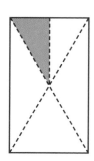

5 Draw two different ways to split these shapes into quarters.

CHALLENGE

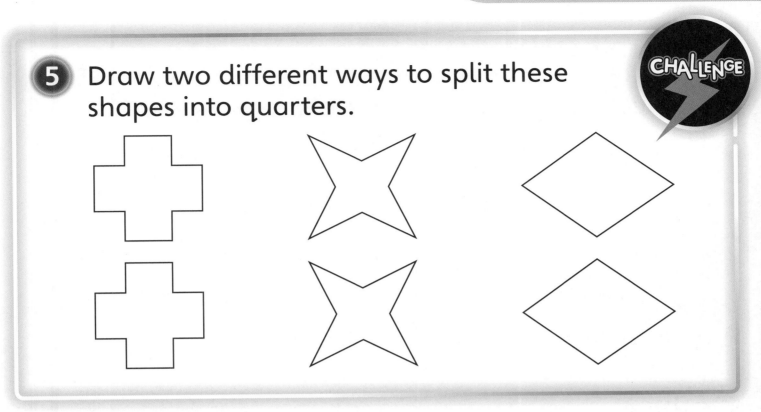

Reflect

Show a quarter on this rectangle.

Use a ruler to draw lines.

I wonder how many ways I can split a rectangle into quarters.

My drawing shows a quarter because

Finding quarters ❷

① Split each group into quarters.

a)

A quarter of 4 is ⬜ .

c)

A quarter of 20 is ⬜ .

b)

A quarter of ⬜ is ⬜ .

d)

A quarter of ⬜ is ⬜ .

② Which shows quarters? Circle your answers.

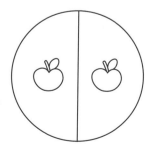  

3 Use one of these words to complete each sentence.

| more than | less than | exactly |

a)

This is _____ a quarter full.

b)

This is _____ a quarter full.

c)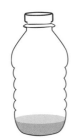

This is _____ a quarter full.

4 Complete the sentences.

a) A quarter of 4 is ☐ .

b) A quarter of 8 is ☐ .

c) A quarter of ☐ is 4.

d) A quarter of ☐ is 1.

I could draw dots or use counters to help.

53

5

I gave 4 to my sister. So that is a quarter.

Ben

Meg

No, that is not enough.

Who is right? Explain your answer.

_____ is right because _____

_____

6 What are the values of 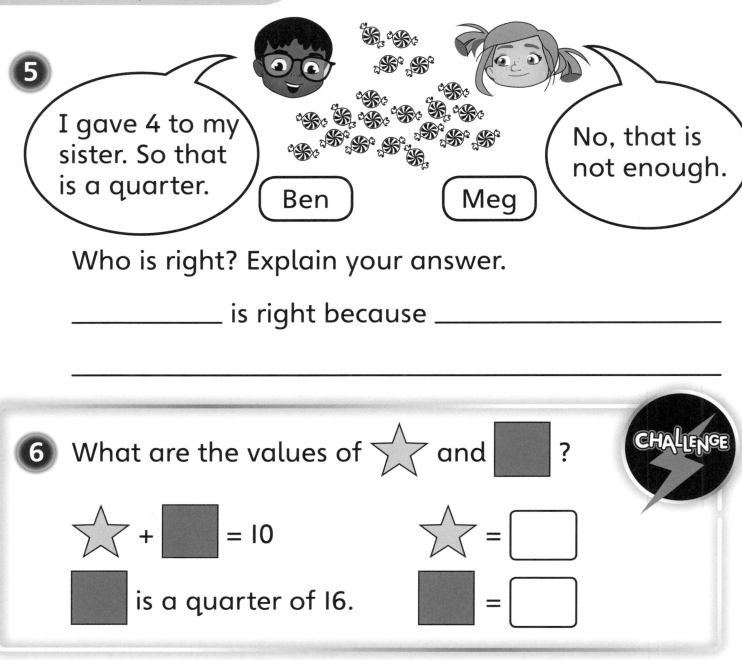 and ☐ ?

CHALLENGE

☆ + ☐ = 10

☐ is a quarter of 16.

☆ = ☐

☐ = ☐

Reflect

- I can find a quarter of 12 by _____
- _____
- _____
-

Solving word problems – halves and quarters

1 **a)** There are 8 .

Half of the ⬭ are eaten.

How many ⬭ are eaten?

Half of 8 ⬭ is ☐ ⬭.

☐ ⬭ are eaten.

b) Here are a quarter of the 🚗 from a toy box.

How many 🚗 in total?

5 is a quarter of ☐.

There are ☐ 🚗 in total.

2 There are 20 pebbles.

Emma paints dots on half of the pebbles.

Bryn paints stripes on a quarter of the pebbles.

Complete the sentences.

a) A _____ of 20 is ☐ .

☐ pebbles have dots.

b) A _____ of 20 is ☐ .

☐ pebbles have stripes.

3 There are 12 birds.

A quarter of the 🐦 fly away.

How many 🐦 are left?

There are ☐ 🐦 left.

4 Michael uses a quarter of the circles and half of the triangles to make a picture.

CHALLENGE

Circle the picture that Michael makes.

A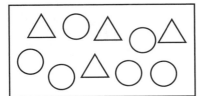

B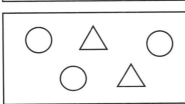

C

D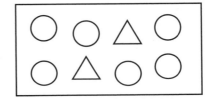

Reflect

Which questions needed you to think about quarters?

_____

Which questions needed you to think about halves?

_____

Which questions were harder? Why?

_____

_____

→ Textbook 1C p80

End of unit check

My journal

Luke says, 'I would like half of them.'

Eva says, 'I would like a quarter, please.'

Luke works out half, but Eva is stuck.

Can you explain why?

It is easier for Luke because _____

_____ .

It is harder for Eva because _____

_____ .

These words might help you.

half   quarter

whole   part

split

Power check

How do you feel about your work in this unit?

Power puzzle

These grids have been half shaded.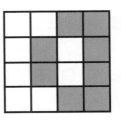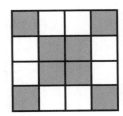

Shade half of each grid.

What different patterns can you make?

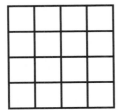

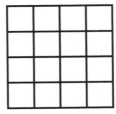

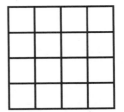

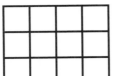

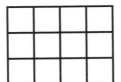

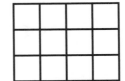

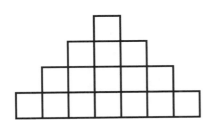

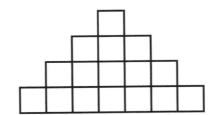

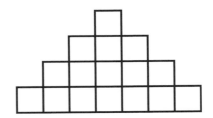

→ Textbook 1C p84

Describing turns

a) Ella is facing the ⬡ .

She makes a half turn.

What is she facing now?

Ella is facing the _____ .

b) Ella is facing the ⬡ .

She makes a whole turn.

What is she facing now?

Ella is facing the _____ .

c) Ella is looking at the ⬡ .

She turns and is now looking at the ⬡ .

What turn did she make?

Ella made a _____ turn.

2 Put a ✔ to show whether the has made the correct turn.

	True	False
quarter turn		
whole turn		
three-quarter turn		

3 Do you agree with Josh?

Circle your answer.   Yes / No.

Explain why.

_____

_____

_____

I have made two quarter turns.

4

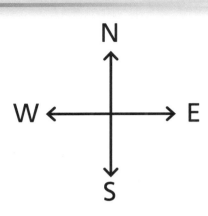

a) Face N and make a half turn.

Which letter do you face now? _____

b) Face W and make a quarter turn .

Which letter do you face now? _____

> I wonder what the letters N, S, E and W mean.

Reflect

Circle a turn.

whole   half   quarter   three-quarter

Draw the turn in the box.

Explain it to a partner.

Describing positions **1**

1

Circle left or right to complete the sentences.

a) The is to the left / right of the .

b) The is to the left / right of the .

c) The is to the left / right of the .

d) The is to the left / right of the .

2

Draw a to the left of the .

63

3 Describe how the horse walked to the stable.

Put the sentences in the correct order using 1, 2 and 3.

Turn 1 quarter turn right. ☐

Walk 6 steps forwards. ☐

Walk 8 steps forwards. ☐

Turn 1 quarter turn left. ☐

I think one sentence will not be used.

4 Complete the sentences to help the get to the pond.

First walk ☐ steps _____ .

Then, turn 1 _____ .

Next, walk ☐ steps _____ .

forwards   left   right

quarter turn   half turn   three-quarter turn

5 Which does not describe the turn of the tractor?

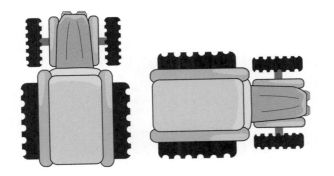

quarter turn right

half turn left

three-quarter turn left

Explain why.

_____

_____

_____

Reflect

Stand up and face your teacher.

Follow these instructions.

1 Make a quarter turn to the left.

2 Make a half turn to the right.

3 Make a three-quarter turn to the right.

What are you facing now? Are you facing the same way as your partner?

→ Textbook 1C p92

Describing positions ❷

1 Here is a grid of animals.

Circle above, below, left or right to complete the sentences.

a) The 🐱 is above / below the 🐘 .

b) The 🐑 is to the left / right of the 🐕 .

c) The 🐯 is above / below the 🐭 and to

the left / right of the 🐄 .

66

2 Draw the missing pictures in the grid using the sentences to help you.

The tree is above the  .

The house is to the left of the  .

3 Describe the position of the socks in three different ways.

hat	T-shirt	dress
shoes	socks	trousers

1 _____

2 _____

3 _____

4 Here is a grid of letters.

Use the clues to find the four-letter word.

a	t	b
k	e	p
d	c	l

a) the letter between d and l   _____

b) the letter to the left of t   _____

c) the letter above d   _____

d) the letter on the middle
row between k and p   _____

Reflect

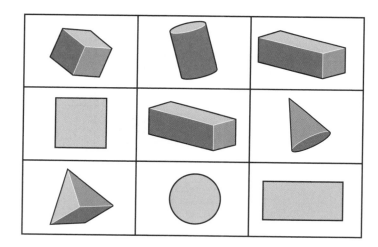

Choose a shape from the grid.

Describe the position of this shape to a partner.

Can your partner guess which shape you chose?

68

End of unit check

My journal

Can you guide the mouse to the cheese?

Can you find more than one path?

These words might help you.

forwards   **backwards**

square   **left**   **right**

half turn   **quarter turn**

three-quarter turn

Power check

How do you feel about your work in this unit?

Power puzzle

Work out the name of each person.

Anya is to the left of the person wearing a hat.

Hassan is in the window below Anya.

Molly is above the person to Katie's right.

Maya is on the top row.

If Bob looks up he can see Molly.

Counting to 100

1 How many buttons are there?

There are ⬜ buttons.

I will put them into groups of 10 first.

Circle the groups of 10.

2 How many 🪧 are there?

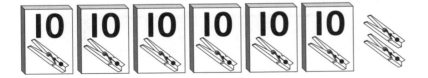

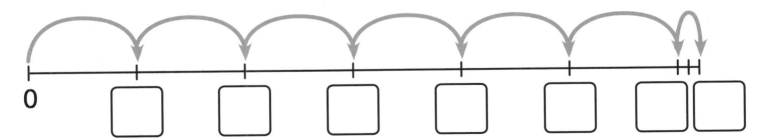

0

There are ⬜ 🪧 .

3 How many  are there?

a)
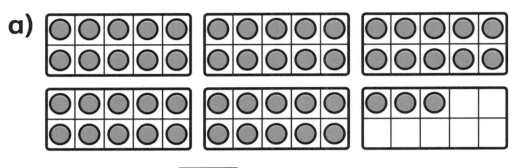

There are ☐ ◯.

b)

There are ☐ ◯.

4 Fill in the missing numbers.

a)

45	46	47				51

b)

69	70		72			75	

c)

64	63	62			

d)

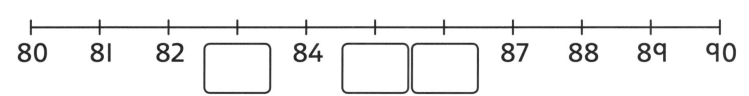

5 Connect the dots.

CHALLENGE

Do I have to count up? Could I do it another way?

Reflect

With your partner, count from 34 to 62.

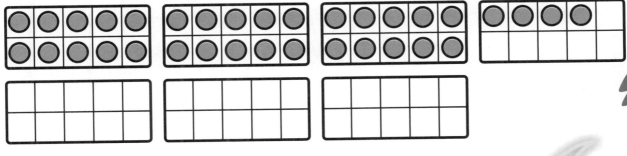

Take it in turns to say a number.

Draw a counter on a square in the [ ] each time.

I can count back from 62 to 40.

→ Textbook 1C p104

Exploring number patterns

1 What number is each shape covering?

1	2	3	4	5	6	7	8	⬠	10
11	12	13	14	15	16	17	18	19	20
21	22	23	24	25	26	27	28	★	30
31	32	33	34	35	36	37	38	39	40
41	■	43	44	45	46	47	48	49	50
51	52	53	54	55	56	57	58	59	60
61	62	63	64	65	▲	67	68	69	●
71	72	73	74	75	76	77	78	79	80
81	82	83	84	85	86	87	88	89	90
91	92	93	94	▱	96	97	98	99	100

■ = ☐

▲ = ☐

● = ☐

⬠ = ☐

▱ = ☐

★ = ☐

2 Fill in the missing numbers.

a)

17	18	19	20
27		29	
	38		40
47		49	

b)

				45			
52	53					57	
				75			

3 Use a number square to help you complete the sentences.

a) One more than 73 is ☐.

b) One more than 29 is ☐.

c) ☐ is one less than 18.

d) ☐ is one more than 46.

e) 39 is _____ than 40.

3, 13, 23, ... 93

4 Freya is counting in tens.

She starts at 3.

Shade in all the numbers she says on the grid.

1	2	3	4	5	6	7	8	9	10
11	12	13	14	15	16	17	18	19	20
21	22	23	24	25	26	27	28	29	30
31	32	33	34	35	36	37	38	39	40
41	42	43	44	45	46	47	48	49	50
51	52	53	54	55	56	57	58	59	60
61	62	63	64	65	66	67	68	69	70
71	72	73	74	75	76	77	78	79	80
81	82	83	84	85	86	87	88	89	90
91	92	93	94	95	96	97	98	99	100

What did you notice?

5 Fill in the missing numbers.

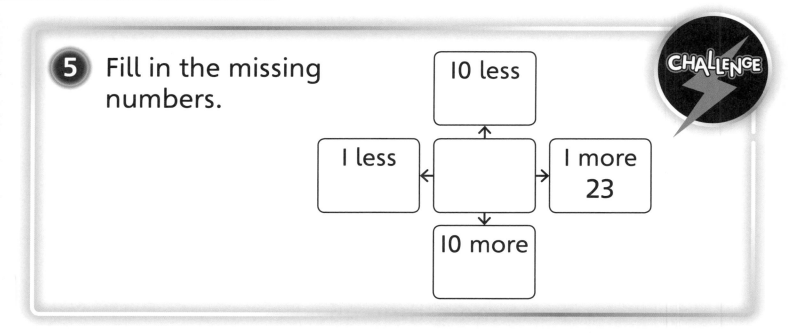

Reflect

Here is a blank 100 square.

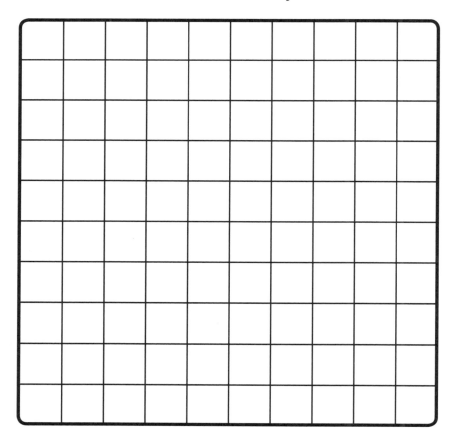

Put the numbers 15, 25 46, 70, and 99 on the 100 square.

Did you get the same answers as your partner?

Give each other numbers to put on the 100 square.

Partitioning numbers

1 **a)** How many are there?

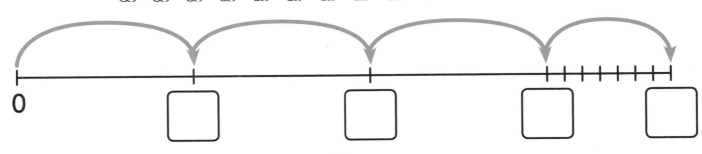

0

There are ⬜ .

b) How many  are there?

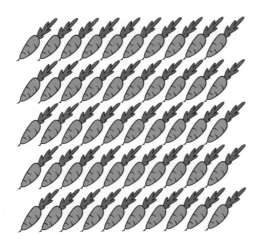

There are ⬜  .

77

2 Match the amounts. Write the number that each place value grid shows.

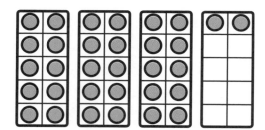

Tens	Ones

Tens	Ones

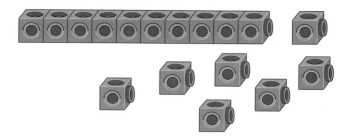

Tens	Ones

3 Complete each number on a place value grid.

Draw ⬜⬜⬜⬜ to represent 10.

Draw ☐ to represent 1.

a) 45

Tens	Ones

b) 20

Tens	Ones

4 Here are some number cards.

| 2 | 5 | 6 |

CHALLENGE

How many different 2-digit numbers can you make?

Pick one of your numbers.

Draw your number.

Make your number.

Reflect

Work with your partner.

Use all the 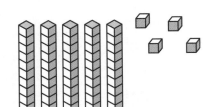 to make two different numbers.

Tens	Ones

Tens	Ones

What number did you make?

What number did your partner make?

→ Textbook 1C p112

Partitioning numbers ❷

1 **a)** How many 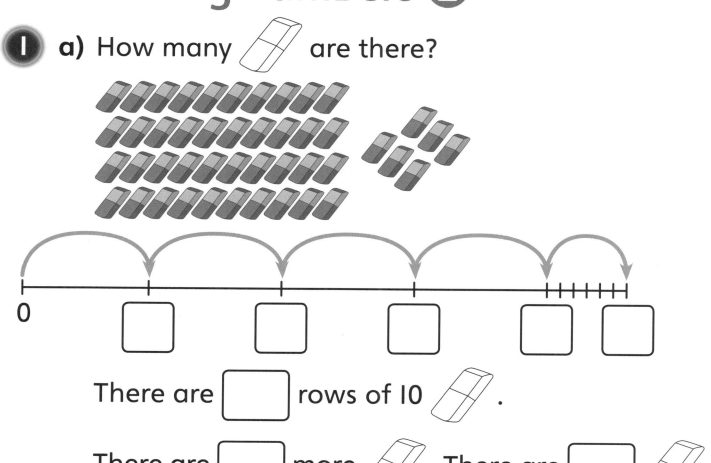 are there?

There are ☐ rows of 10 🔲 .

There are ☐ more 🔲 . There are ☐ 🔲 .

b) How many ✏️ are there?

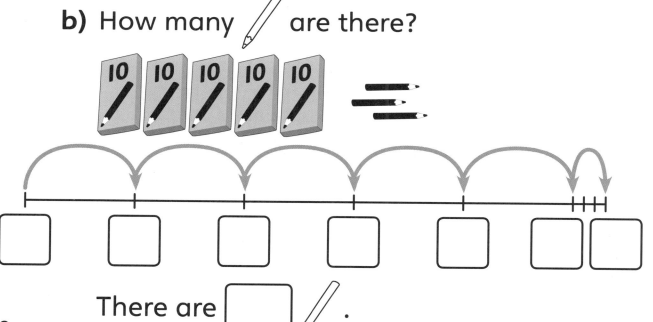

There are ☐ ✏️ .

80

2 Complete each diagram and number sentence.

a)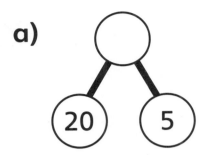

b)

Tens	Ones

☐ = 20 + 5   ☐ = 90 + 7

3 Complete each number fact.

a) 4 tens and 5 ones = ☐   e) ☐ = 30 + 6

b) 8 tens and 6 ones = ☐   f) 50 + 4 = ☐

c) ☐ tens and 3 ones = 73   g) 29 = ☐ + 9

d) I ten and ☐ ones = 10   h) 60 = 52 + ☐

4 Use up all of the to make two 💡 different numbers.

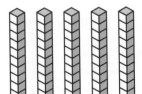

Tens	Ones

Tens	Ones

What numbers did you make?

☐ = ☐ + ☐   ☐ = ☐ + ☐

5 Use the number cards.

| 2 | 5 | 6 | 7 |

CHALLENGE

a) Make a number with 5 tens. ☐

b) Make a number with 5 ones. ☐

c) Make a number that has more tens than ones. ☐

d) Make the number that is 10 less than 36. ☐

Reflect

Roll two dice. Use the scores to make a 2-digit number.

Draw it.

Make it.

Write it as tens and ones.

  = 23

Comparing numbers ❶

1 Who planted more flowers?

_____ planted more than _____ .

2 Complete the number sentences using <, > or =.

a)

47 ◯ 32

b)

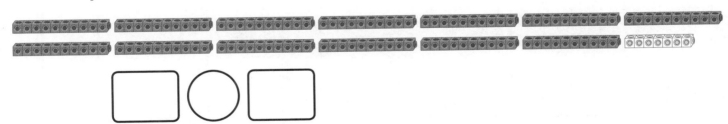

[ ] ◯ [ ]

c)

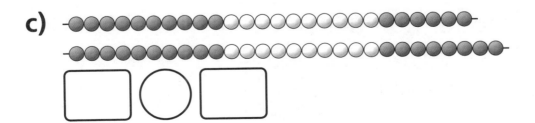

[ ] ◯ [ ]

3 **a)** Which number is greater?

Tens	Ones
3	4

Tens	Ones
2	9

The greater number is ☐.

This is because ☐ ◯ ☐.

I lined the ▱▱▱▱ up to help me compare the numbers.

b) Which number is smaller?

Tens	Ones

Tens	Ones

The smaller number is ☐.

This is because ☐ ◯ ☐.

4 Draw to make the sentence true.

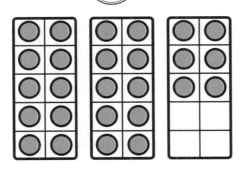 >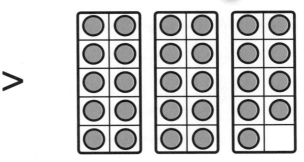

5 Draw on the  and the ▭ to keep these sentences true.

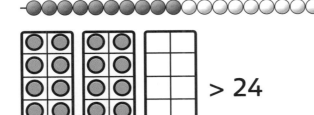 < 24

> 24

CHALLENGE

I think I should make the numbers first.

Reflect

How can you compare these two numbers?

Tens	Ones
6	6

Tens	Ones
7	2

Show your partner.

→ Textbook 1C p120

Comparing numbers ❷

 Write 'greater than', 'less than' or 'equal to' to compare the numbers. Then use <, > or = to complete the number sentence.

a)

Tens	Ones		Tens	Ones

25 is _____ 28

This is because ☐ ◯ ☐ .

b)

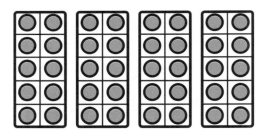

40 is _____ 40

☐ ◯ ☐ .

Remember to compare the tens first and then the ones.

86

2 Compare the following numbers using <, > or =.

a)

Tens	Ones
6	4

Tens	Ones
4	8

64 ◯ 48

b)

Tens	Ones
9	0

Tens	Ones
9	5

90 ◯ 95

c) 23 ◯ 28

d) 33 ◯ 33

e) 72 ◯ 27

f) 55 ◯ 5

3 In each pair, circle the smallest number.

a) 39 and 49

b) 9 and 11

4 In each pair, circle the greatest number.

a) 72 and 75

b) 19 and 9

5 Put a **different** digit in each box to make the number statements correct.

| 6 | 7 | < | 6 | |

| 6 | | < | 6 | 7 |

| 5 | 7 | < | | 8 |

Reflect

How can you compare 54 and 58?

How can you compare 15 and 76?

Ordering numbers

1 Which has the greatest number of marbles?

Circle your answer.

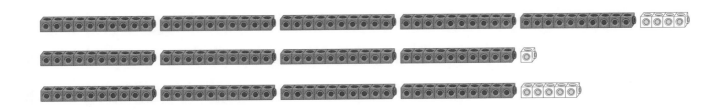

2 Put the numbers in order from smallest to greatest.

Tens	Ones
4	4

Tens	Ones
5	8

Tens	Ones
2	8

⬚ , ⬚ , ⬚

3 Order the following numbers from smallest to greatest.

a) 72, 65, 63

☐ < ☐ < ☐

b) 11, 38, 30, 48

_____

4 Order the following numbers from greatest to smallest.

a) 48, 47, 64

☐ > ☐ > ☐

b) 13, 30, 33, 31

_____

5 Here are some number cards.

| 3 | 6 | 8 | 9 |

a) What is the smallest 2-digit number you can make?

☐☐

b) What is the greatest 2-digit number you can make?

☐☐

6 If the following numbers are put in order, which number would be in the middle?

CHALLENGE

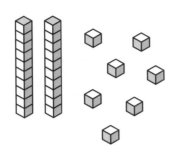 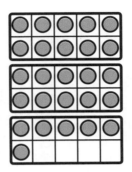

_____

Reflect

| 44 | 61 | 40 | 54 |

Put these numbers in order from smallest to greatest.

_____

How did you do it?

_____

→ Textbook 1C p128

Bonds to 100 ❶

1 Use the  to help you write the number bonds to 100.

a)

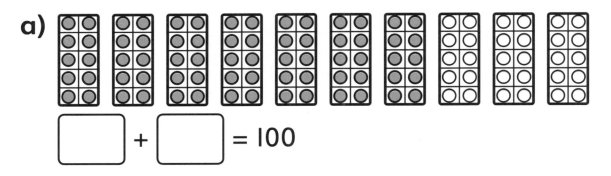

[ ] + [ ] = 100

b)

[ ] + [ ] = 100

c)

100	
60	?

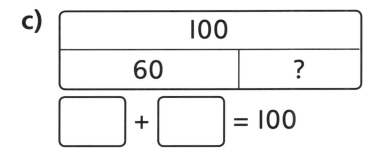

[ ] + [ ] = 100

2 Colour in some of the ◯ to show the bond to 100.

20 + 80 = 100

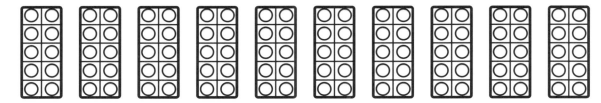

3 **a)** Complete each 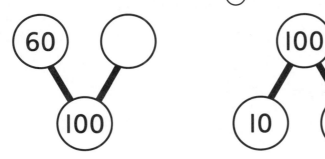.

60   ◯

100

100   ◯

10   ◯

b) Complete the fact family for one of the above.

◯ + ◯ = ◯

◯ − ◯ = ◯

◯ + ◯ = ◯

◯ − ◯ = ◯

4 Complete each number fact.

a) 40 + ◯ = 100   50 + ◯ = 100

30 + ◯ = 100   0 = 100 − ◯

100 − ◯ = 10   100 − 20 = ◯

b) 60 + 40 = 30 + ◯   10 + ◯ = 90 + ◯

5 The total of each row is shown at the end.

CHALLENGE

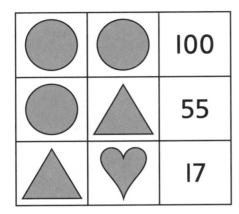

		100
		55
		17

What is the value of each symbol?

⬤ = ☐   ▲ = ☐   ♥ = ☐

Reflect

How many bonds to 100 can you write down?

☐ **0** + ☐ **0** = 100

Are there any the same?

Did you get any your partner did not get?

Bonds to 100 ❷

1

1	2	3	4	5	6	7	8	9	10
11	12	13	14	15	16	17	18	19	20
21	22	23	24	25	26	27	28	29	30
31	32	33	34	35	36	37	38	39	40
41	42	43	44	45	46	47	48	49	50
51	52	53	54	55	56	57	58	59	60
61	62	63	64	65	66	67	68	69	70
71	72	73	74	75	76	77	78	79	80
81	82	83	84	85	86	87	88	89	90
91	92	93	94	95	96	97	98	99	100

a) There are 10 rows.

There are ☐ rows shaded.

There are ☐ rows not shaded.

☐ + ☐ = 10

b) There are 100 squares.

There are ☐ squares shaded.

There are ☐ squares not shaded.

☐ + ☐ = 100

2 Write the number bonds that are shown.

a)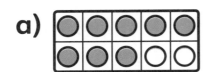

$\boxed{} + \boxed{} = 10$

b)

$\boxed{} + \boxed{} = 10$

3 Circle the bonds to 10.

| 7 + 3 | 5 + 5 | 4 + 8 | 1 + 0 | 2 + 8 | 10 – 5 |

Circle the bonds to 100.

| 40 + 50 | 90 + 10 | 10 + 90 | 70 + 50 | 100 + 0 | 60 + 4 | 20 + 80 |

4 Complete each number bond.

a) $5 + \boxed{} = 10$

$50 + \boxed{} = 100$

b) $\boxed{} + 8 = 10$

$80 + \boxed{} = 100$

c) $100 - \boxed{} = 70$

$\boxed{} - 3 = 7$

d) $20 + \boxed{} = 100$

$\boxed{} - 20 = 80$

96

5

CHALLENGE

Each ⬜ contains 10 🍎.

2 of the bags contain green 🍏.

The rest contain red 🍎.

How many red 🍎 are there?

There are ⬜ red 🍎.

Reflect

Pick a card.

| 0 | 10 | 20 | 30 | 40 | 50 | 60 | 70 | 80 | 90 | 100 |

Tell your partner your card.

Ask your partner to choose the card that makes the bond to 100.

Did they get it correct? How do you know?

→ Textbook 1C p136

End of unit check

My journal

Complete the target number grid.

Target number of 75

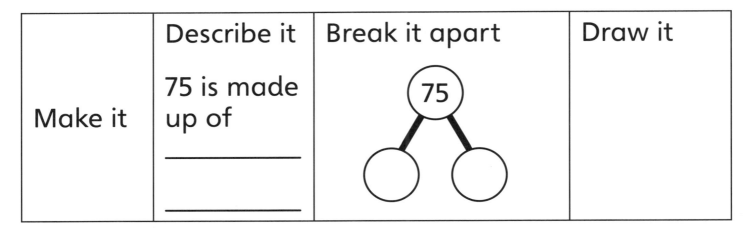

Make it	Describe it 75 is made up of _____ _____	Break it apart 75	Draw it

Why not try it with different target numbers?

These words might help you.

more   **less**

tens   **ones**

Power check

How do you feel about your work in this unit?

Power play

A game for 2 to 4 players.

Round 1

Shade in a 2-digit number on the grid.

It can go left to right or downwards.

6	7	4	6	3	1
9	5	2	8	3	7
8	1	0	1	5	6
4	4	3	0	1	7
3	2	8	2	9	8
5	7	4	7	3	0

| 8 | 2 | = 82

$\dfrac{8}{4}$ = 84

Compare your number with your partner.

The player with the larger number scores a point.

Round 2

Shade in two squares next to each other.

The player with the smaller number scores a point.

Repeat from the start until a player scores 4 points.

You may not shade a square more than once.

→ Textbook 1C p140

Using before and after

1 Label the **before** and **after** pictures.

a)

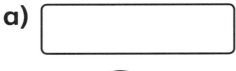

b)

c)

2 Put these pictures in the right order.

Number them I to 3 to show the right order.

3 These are the activities that Noah did this week.

| Sunday | Monday | Tuesday | Wednesday |

| Thursday | Friday | Saturday |

a) What did he do the day before Monday?

_____

b) What did he do the day after Wednesday?

_____

4 Underline the days before Thursday.

Circle the days after Thursday.

Sunday	Monday	Tuesday	Wednesday	Thursday	Friday	Saturday

5 **a)** What day is it today?

_____

b) What day was it yesterday?

_____

c) What day is it tomorrow?

_____

If you give a different answer to the first question, do the other answers change?

Reflect

Look at the picture.

What could have happened before?

What might happen after?

Share your ideas with a partner.

Using a calendar

1 Underline today.

Circle yesterday.

Colour tomorrow.

Sunday	Monday	Tuesday	Wednesday	Thursday	Friday	Saturday

2 When are these activities happening?

August

S	M	T	W	T	F	S
		1	2	3	4	5
6	7	8	9	10	11	12
13	14	15	16	17	18	19
20	21	22	23	24	25	26
27	28	29	30	31		

a)

The month is _____.

The number day in the month is ☐.

The day of the week is _____.

b)

The month is _____.

The number day in the month is ☐.

The day of the week is _____.

3

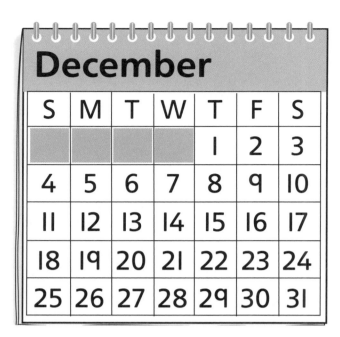

a) Which day of the week is the first day of the month? _____.

b) Which day of the week is 6 December?

_____.

c) How many Thursdays are in December? ⬜.

d) Draw a ☆ on the last Tuesday of the month.

e) Draw a ✕ on 20 December.

f) Which day of the week is 20 December?

_____.

4 Number the months in the correct order.

January ☐

February ☐

May ☐

March ☐

April ☐

July ☐

August ☐

June ☐

November ☐

September ☐

October ☐

December ☐

> I have made some mistakes here.

> I used a calendar to help me.

Reflect

Today, I have used a calendar to:

- _____
- _____
- _____

→ Textbook 1C p148

Telling time to the hour

1 Match the times to the clocks.

12 o'clock

8 o'clock

1 o'clock

2 What time is it?

a)

b)

c)

[ ] o'clock

[ ] o'clock

[ ] o'clock

3 Draw the times.

a)
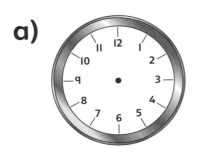

10 o'clock

b)
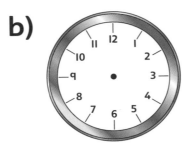

2 o'clock

c)
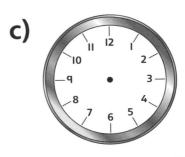

7 o'clock

4 Who is right? Circle your answer.

The minute hand is pointing to the 12, so it is 12 o'clock.

That is not right. The hour hand is pointing to the 5, so it is 5 o'clock.

12 o'clock

5 o'clock

5

The minute hand is pointing to the 12. The hour hand is pointing to a number with a 1 in it.

What times could it be?

_____

I wonder how many answers I can think of.

What do you do at these different times of day?

_____

_____

Reflect

A clock shows 4 o'clock.

Draw what it looks like.

Telling time to the half hour

1 Match the times to the clocks.

half past 5

half past 8

half past 6

half past 7

2 What time is it?

a)

 half past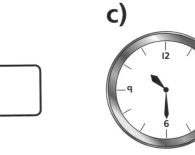

c)

half past ☐

b)

 half past ☐

d)

 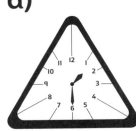 half past ☐

3 Draw the times.

a)

half past 2

c)

half past 3

b)

half past 4

d)

half past 9

4 Is Astrid right?

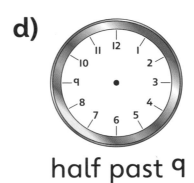

This one is easy. It is half past 6.

Circle the correct answer. Yes No

Explain why.

_____

_____

5

CHALLENGE

The minute hand is pointing to the 6. The hour hand is pointing in between two numbers that are less than 5.

What time could it be?

_____

_____

I can think of more than one answer.

What do you do at these different times of day?

_____

Reflect

A clock shows half past 7. Draw what it looks like.

→ **Textbook 1C p156**

Writing time

1 How long do these activities take?

 A night's sleep

seconds

 Eating a biscuit

minutes

 Playing football

hours

2 Choose the right word to complete these sentences.

seconds   minutes   hours

a) 'It took me 3 _____ to eat a sandwich.'

b) 'It took me 3 _____ to fly to another country for a holiday.'

3 Ask your partner to use a timer and count how many times you can hop on one leg in 1 minute.

I can hop ☐ times in 1 minute.

4 Are they both right?

It took you 60 seconds!

It took you 1 minute!

Circle the correct answer.

Yes   No

How do you know?

_____

_____

5 How many times can you write your name in 40 seconds?

CHALLENGE

Ask a partner to use a timer to measure 40 seconds while you write.

I wrote my name [ ] times in 40 seconds.

Now time your partner doing the same activity.

Who was faster?
Who has the shorter name?

Reflect

What can you do in I minute?

- _____
- _____
- _____

What can you do in I hour?

- _____
- _____
- _____

Comparing time

1 Compare the times and circle the correct words.

20 minutes

12 minutes

20 minutes

12 minutes

a) 20 is a **greater** / **smaller** number than 12.

b) 20 minutes is **less time** / **more time** than 12 minutes.

c) 20 minutes is **longer** / **shorter** than 12 minutes.

d) It takes Lucy 20 minutes to get to school. This is **faster** / **slower** than 12 minutes.

2 Which time is faster?

I took 20 minutes.

I took 18 minutes.

⬜ minutes is faster than ⬜ minutes.

3 Circle the correct words to complete the sentences.

6 hours   12 hours   2 hours

a) 2 hours is **shorter** / **longer** than 12 hours.

b) So the helicopter is **faster** / **slower** than the bicycle.

c) 6 hours is **shorter** / **longer** than 2 hours.

d) So the car is **faster** / **slower** than the helicopter.

4

I slept for 12 hours last night.

I slept for more than 6 hours. But I slept less than you.

CHALLENGE

Joe

Amy

How many hours of sleep could Amy have had?

She could have had ☐ hours of sleep.

Reflect

Circle the longest time and underline the shortest time.

15 seconds   10 hours   18 minutes   16 minutes

Explain your answer to your partner.

→ Textbook 1C p164

Solving word problems – time

1 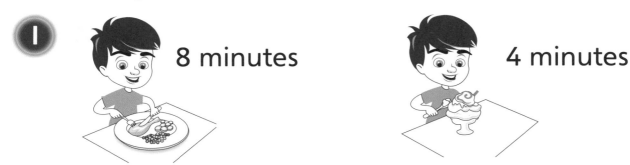 8 minutes   4 minutes

How long does Jack's meal take altogether?

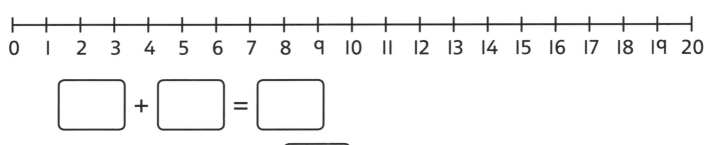

☐ + ☐ = ☐

Jack's meal takes ☐ minutes.

2

4 minutes have gone by.

The test is 18 minutes long.

How long does Claire have left?

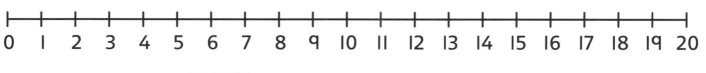

Claire has ☐ minutes left.

3 Tariq used a timer to count down from 20 seconds.

When he had finished building his tower there were 5 seconds left on his timer.

I counted down from 20 seconds.

I took 16 seconds altogether!

Tariq

Sue

Who was faster?

_____ was faster.

Explain why.

_____

_____

4 What time will it be in four hours' time?

 It will be _____.

5

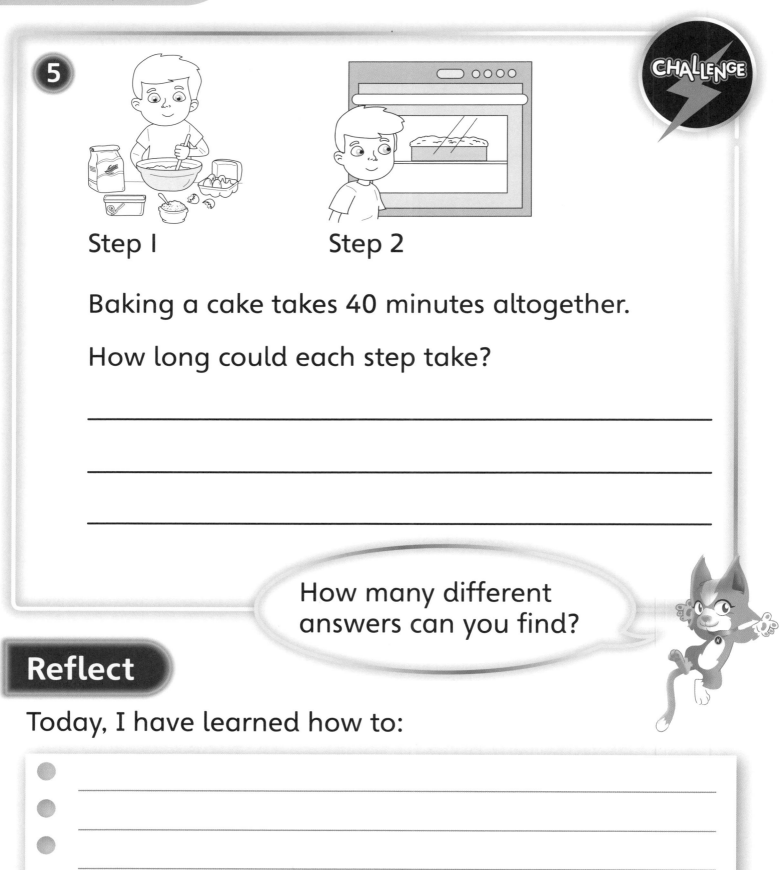

CHALLENGE

Step 1

Step 2

Baking a cake takes 40 minutes altogether.

How long could each step take?

_____

_____

_____

How many different
answers can you find?

Reflect

Today, I have learned how to:

_____

_____

_____

End of unit check

My journal

Look at these two clocks.

What's the same?

What's different?

These words might help you.

minute hand

hour hand

half past

Power check

How do you feel about your work in this unit?

Power puzzle

Clever clocks

Use a clock to make one of these times to show your partner.

5 o'clock	half past 10	7 o'clock	2 o'clock
half past 7	1 o'clock	half past 12	11 o'clock
half past 1	6 o'clock	half past 5	half past 6
12 o'clock	half past 2	10 o'clock	half past 11

If your partner can work out which time you are showing, they should colour it in.

Take it in turns.

Who colours in the most times?

Recognising coins

1 Match the coin to the correct word.

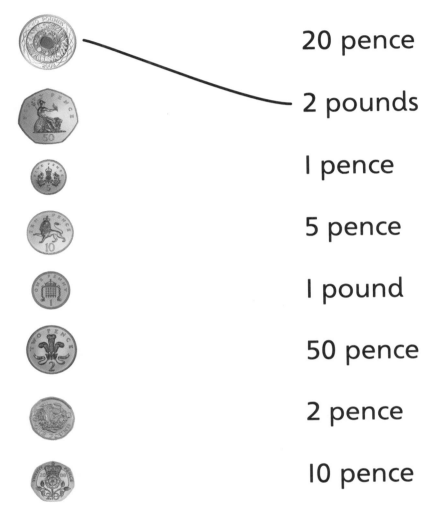

20 pence

2 pounds

1 pence

5 pence

1 pound

50 pence

2 pence

10 pence

2 I have 3  and 4 . What coin is hidden?

There is a ☐ pence coin hidden.

3 Draw a line to show where each coin should go.

Less than 10 pence		Greater than 10 pence

4 Which coins go in the empty boxes?

Draw a line from the correct coin to the empty box.

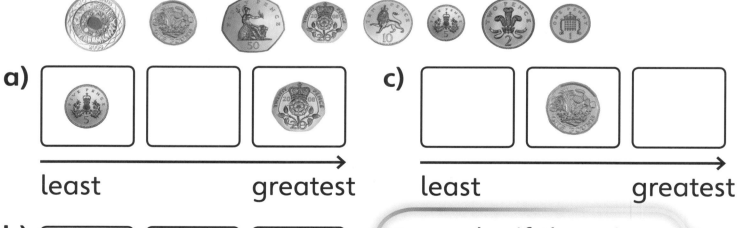

a)

least   greatest

c)

least   greatest

b)

least   greatest

I wonder if there is more than one coin that could go into any of the empty boxes?

5 Circle coins and fill the gaps to complete the table.

CHALLENGE

	5 pence	Greater than 2 pence
	20 pence	Less than _____
	☐ pence	Greater than _____
	☐ pence	Less than 20 pence

Reflect

I could ask about the colour, the size or whether its value is greater than or less than another coin.

Ask your friend to think of a coin.

What coin is your friend thinking of?

You can ask them three questions about it.

→ **Textbook 1C p176**

Recognising notes

1 Match each group of notes to the right amount.

One 20 pound note

Four 10 pound notes

Two 10 pound notes

Two 5 pound notes

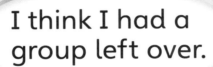 I think I had a group left over.

2 Joe has three 10 pound notes, one 20 pound note and two 50 pound notes. Which note is missing?

The _____ note is missing.

3 Count how many there are of each note.

a) There are ☐ 5 pound notes.

b) There are ☐ 10 pound notes.

c) There are ☐ 20 pound notes.

d) There are ☐ 50 pound notes.

4 Use <, > or = to complete the sentences.

a)  £20 note ◯ 10 pounds

b) 50 pounds ◯ £50 note

c)  £5 note ◯ £10 note

127

5 Charlie has put the notes in order from greatest value to least value.

Circle the one in the wrong place.

Explain why it is wrong.

_____

_____

_____

Reflect

Circle all the real notes.

Tell your partner which notes are not real.

Counting with coins

1 How much is each group of coins worth?

a)  ☐ pence

5, 10, 15, 20, ____ .

b)  ☐ pence

c)  ☐ pence

d)  ☐ pence

2 Draw the coins to match the amounts.

a) 8 pence in 1 pence coins

b) 8 pence in 2 pence coins

129

3 Draw the coins to match the amounts.

a) 10 pence in 5 pence coins

b) 10 pence in 10 pence coins

4 Use <, > or = to complete each number sentence.

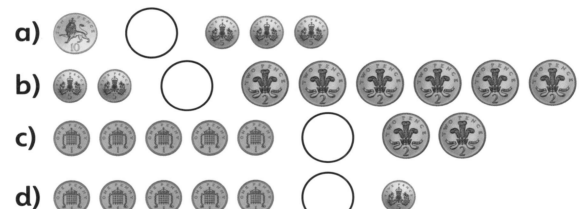

5 Jack has a wallet with only coins in it.

He says he has 9 pence altogether.

Is Jack correct?

_____

I drew 2 pence coins to help me count how much money Jack might have.

6 Lucy has 6 silver coins.

Pavel has 3 silver coins.

They have the same amount of money.

Which coins do they have?

I wonder which coins are silver. I will look at some real coins!

Reflect

Use 1 pence coins, 2 pence coins, 5 pence coins and 10 pence coins.

Using one type of coin each time, how many ways can you make 20 pence?

→ Textbook 2C p184

End of unit check

My journal

How many ways can you make 20 pence using ,

 and ?

You can use each coin more than once.

These words might help you.

pence   coin

five   ten   two

is equal to

Power check

How do you feel about your work in this unit?

Power play

Get into pairs or teams.

The first team chooses up to 5 of **one** kind of coin from
 , and .

The second team asks questions to help guess the amount.

The first team can only answer yes or no.

Example:

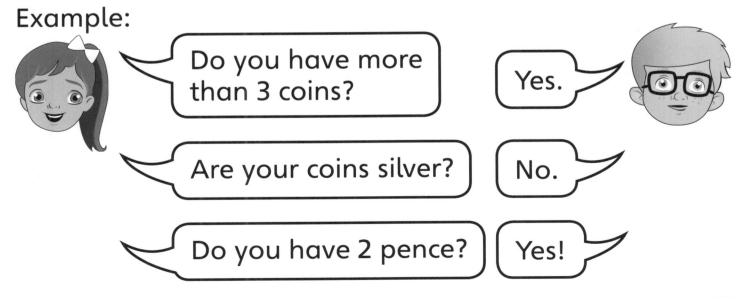

Do you have more than 3 coins?

Yes.

Are your coins silver?

No.

Do you have 2 pence?

Yes!

My Power Points

Colour in the ☆ to show what you have learned.

Colour in the ☺ if you feel happy about what you have learned.

Unit 12

I can ...

☆ ☺ Count in 10s, 5s and 2s

☆ ☺ Make equal groups and add them to find the total

☆ ☺ Make an array

☆ ☺ Double a number

Unit 13

I can ...

☆ ☺ Make equal groups

☆ ☺ Share things equally

Unit 14

I can ...

☆ ☺ Find half of a shape

☆ ☺ Find half of a small number

☆ ☺ Find a quarter of a shape

☆ ☺ Find a quarter using equal sharing

Unit 15

I can …

☆ ☺ Talk about half, quarter and three-quarter turns

☆ ☺ Use words like up, down, left and right to say where something is

Unit 16

I can …

☆ ☺ Count in 10s to 100

☆ ☺ Use a 100 square to look for a pattern

☆ ☺ Use tens and ones to help me count bigger numbers

☆ ☺ Compare two numbers and say which is more and less

☆ ☺ Put numbers in order

☆ ☺ Make number bonds of 100

Unit 17

I can …

☆ ☺ Use the words before and after to talk about time

☆ ☺ Find the day of the week and the date on a calendar

☆ ☺ Read an o'clock time and a half-past time on a clock

☆ ☺ Work out how long something will take

☆ ☺ Use the words shorter, longer, faster and slower to compare time

Unit 18

I can …

☆ ☺ Say the name of all coins when I see them

☆ ☺ Say the name of all notes when I see them

☆ ☺ Count coins

Look at what you put on the first page. Did you do what you said? Could you do even better?